CONTENTS

SPACE RACE

After World War II, the United States and the Soviet Union took opposite sides in a war of spying and propaganda, called the 'Cold War'. Both sides recruited German scientists who had worked on the V-2 rocket programme and hoped to conquer space to show their nation's superiority.

FIRST MAN IN SPACE

People in the USA believed that their technology was more advanced than that of the Soviets. It was, therefore, a great shock to the American public when, on 4 October 1957, the Soviets launched the first satellite, Sputnik 1, into space. Four months later, after many failures, the USA finally launched a satellite, *Explorer I*, into space. The 'Space Race' had begun. But on 12 April 1961, the USA suffered another dent in its national pride when a Soviet cosmonaut, Yuri Gagarin, became the first human in space. Alan Shepard, the first American astronaut, made it into space 23 days later. The Soviets continued to claim 'firsts' - for the first woman in space (Valentina Tereshkova in 1963) and the first space walk (Aleksei Leonov in 1965).

MAN ON THE MOON

The USA started the *Apollo* programme with a plan to beat the Soviets to a first manned moon landing. The Soviets landed unmanned probes on the moon before the Americans, but they had several failures and eventually dropped out of the race. On 20 July 1969, American astronaut Neil Armstrong stepped on the moon. America had at last beaten the Soviets in the final stage of the 'Space Race'.

1

1. *The Soviet* Sputnik, *the first satellite.*
2. *Yuri Gagarin and Valentina Tereshkova (inset).*
3. *Aleksei Leonov, making the first space walk.*
4. *The first American astronauts (Alan Shepard is top left).*
5. *The* Apollo 11 *mission landed on the moon. The astronauts were Neil Armstrong, Michael Collins and Edwin Aldrin.*
6. *Edwin Aldrin on the moon, taken by Neil Armstrong.*

GRAPHIC DISCOVERIES
INCREDIBLE
SPACE MISSIONS

by Gary Jeffrey

illustrated by Mike Lacey

FRANKLIN WATTS
LONDON•SYDNEY

First published in 2009 by Franklin Watts

Franklin Watts
338 Euston Road
London NW1 3BH

Franklin Watts Australia
Level 17/207 Kent Street
Sydney, NSW 2000

A CIP catalogue record for this book is available from the British Library.

Dewey number: 629.4'1

ISBN: 978 0 7496 9239 1

Franklin Watts is a division of Hachette Children's Books, an Hachette UK company.
www.hachette.co.uk

GRAPHIC DISCOVERIES: INCREDIBLE SPACE MISSIONS produced for Franklin
Watts by David West Children's Books, 7 Princeton Court, 55 Felsham Road,
London SW15 1AZ

Copyright © 2009 David West Children's Books

Editor: Gail Bushnell

Photo credits:
All photos courtesy of NASA

629.45

Printed in China

J265.281
€16.00

Website disclaimer:
Note to parents and teachers: Every effort has been made by the Publishers to ensure
that the websites in this book are suitable for children, that they are of the highest
educational value, and that they contain no inappropriate or offensive material.
However, because of the nature of the Internet, it is impossible to guarantee that the
contents of these sites will not be altered. We strongly advise that the Internet is
supervised by a responsible adult.

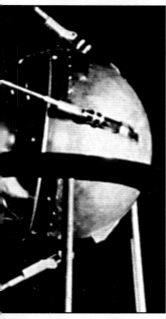

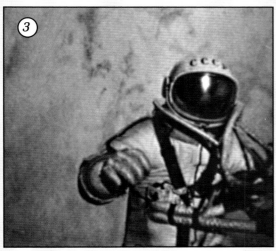

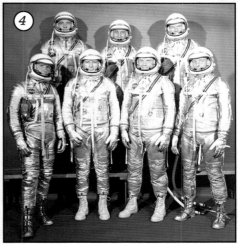

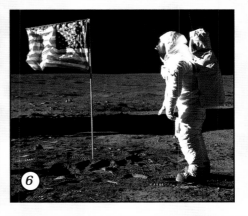

EARLY SPACE TECHNOLOGY

Both the USA and the Soviets continued their space programmes after the moon landing. Exciting advances in technology saw a 'car' driven on the moon and people living in space stations orbiting the Earth.

COLD WAR THAWS IN SPACE

The USA sent six further missions to the moon, one of which didn't land (see page 29). The last was *Apollo 17,* sent in December 1972. After this, manned space missions concentrated on orbiting space stations. Having decided against manned moon exploration, the Soviets had sent a series of *Salyut* space stations into orbit. Understanding the problems of living in space for long periods was essential for future long-distance, manned space journeys. In 1973, the USA sent *Skylab*, their first space station, into orbit. Compared with the *Salyuts* it was massive, but from the beginning it was bugged with problems. It eventually fell to Earth in 1979. It was during the seventies that the two sides started to cooperate on joint space missions. In 1975, an *Apollo* and *Soyuz* docked together and the crews shook hands. The Soviet Union went on to build the *Mir* space station. It was assembled in orbit between 1986 and 1996. Astronauts from many countries spent time on it until it finally fell to Earth in 2001.

Vostok 1
Yuri Gagarin made his historic flight in the Vostok 1 *spacecraft.*

Equipment module

Reentry capsule

Saturn V *launch vehicle* (Apollo)

Vostok 1 *launch vehicle*

Apollo 11 *command/service module*
The command module docked with the lunar module so that the crews could transfer.

Ascent stage

Service module

Command module

Descent stage

Lunar rover
The Apollo 15 to 17 missions took a battery powered 'car' to the moon. It was unfolded from the base of the descent stage and allowed the astronauts to explore much further.

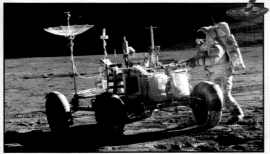

Lunar module
This was called the Eagle on the Apollo 11 mission. When the astronauts left the moon the ascent stage split from the base (descent stage).

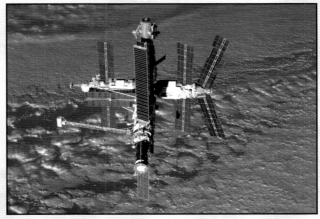

Orbiting space stations
Skylab (left) had a set of solar panels ripped off at launch but still operated for six years. Mir (above) was very successful, despite having a spaceship crash into it and a fire on board!

THE FIRST SPACE WALK

18 MARCH 1965, ABOVE SOUTHERN EUROPE...

THIS IS GROUND CONTROL TO VOSKHOD 2. HAVE YOU FINISHED EXTENDING YOUR AIRLOCK, OVER?

SO, COLONEL LEONOV, ARE YOU READY TO MAKE HISTORY?

AFFIRMATIVE. VOLGA IS PRESSURISED AND READY.

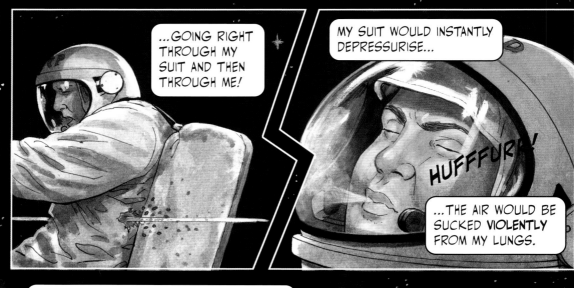

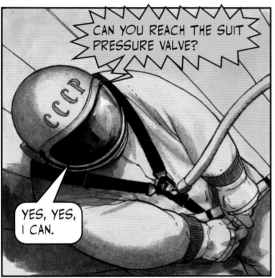

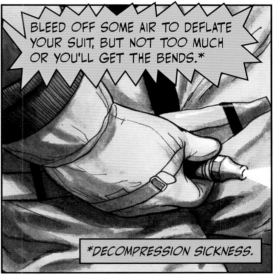

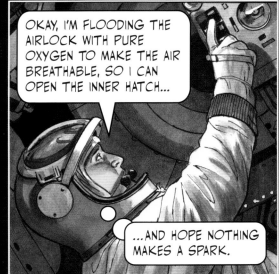

THE END

APOLLO 11
THE MOON LANDING

MAY 25 1961...

"I BELIEVE THIS NATION SHOULD COMMIT ITSELF TO ACHIEVING THE GOAL, BEFORE THIS DECADE IS OUT, OF LANDING A MAN ON THE MOON AND RETURNING HIM SAFELY TO EARTH."

16 JULY 1969, LAUNCH COMPLEX 39-A, KENNEDY SPACE CENTER, FLORIDA...

...T MINUS TEN MINUTES AND COUNTING...

PROJECT GEMINI

...MILLIONS OF DOLLARS, EIGHT YEARS OF RESEARCH AND IT BOILS DOWN TO THIS...

EARLIER TODAY

...THREE MEN, PERCHED ON TOP OF A 3,000-TONNE ROCKET, AIMED AT THE MOON!

MISSION COMMANDER NEIL ARMSTRONG HAS AN ABORT HANDLE BY HIS KNEE, SO IF ANYTHING GOES WRONG DURING THE LAUNCH...

HEY, NEIL, WATCH YOUR POCKET ON THE HANDLE!

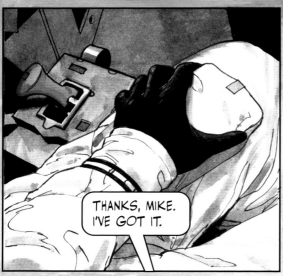

THANKS, MIKE. I'VE GOT IT.

MIKE COLLINS IS THE COMMAND MODULE PILOT.

YOU DON'T WANT THE MISSION TO END PREMATURELY!

HOLD ON TO YOUR HATS, WE'RE ABOUT READY TO SHAKE, RATTLE AND ROLL!

BUZZ ALDRIN IS THE LUNAR MODULE PILOT.

09:32...

...10, ...9, ...IGNITING MAIN BOOSTER!

APOLLO 11 IS TRAVELLING AT 39,000 KILOMETRES PER HOUR (24,000 MPH).

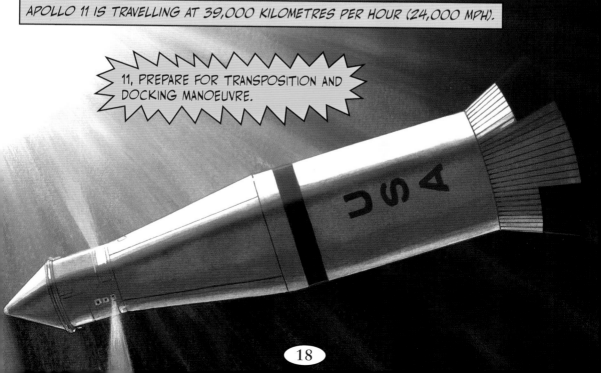

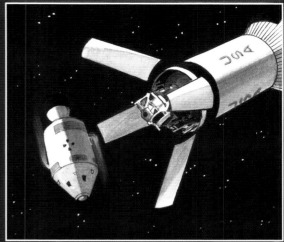

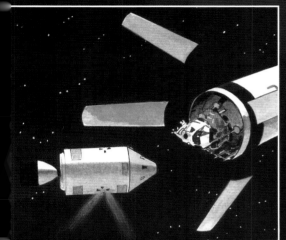

COLUMBIA* HAS DOCKED WITH EAGLE**. PREPARING TO JETTISON THIRD STAGE.

*THE COMMAND/SERVICE MODULE.
**THE LUNAR MODULE.

COPY THAT, HOUSTON. OUT.

SEPARATION COMPLETE. THIRD STAGE IS VENTING.

LET'S GET SOME SLEEP.

1,828 METRES ABOVE THE LUNAR SURFACE...

HOUSTON, I HAVE A PROGRAMME ALARM ...IT'S A 1202.

COPY THAT, NEIL.

STEVE?

IT'S JUST A COMPUTER OVERLOAD. TELL THEM TO KEEP GOING.

ASTRONAUT CHARLIE DUKE IS THE DUTY CAPCOM (CAPSULE COMMUNICATOR).

STEVE BALES IS A LUNAR MODULE FLIGHT CONTROLLER.

YOU ARE 'GO' TO CONTINUE POWERED DESCENT.

JEEZ! THE SURFACE LOOKS SO CLOSE...

914 METRES ABOVE THE LUNAR SURFACE...

ANOTHER ALARM...A 1201 - CAN YOU GIVE ME A READING ON THAT?

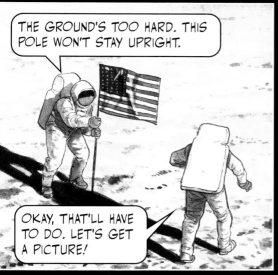

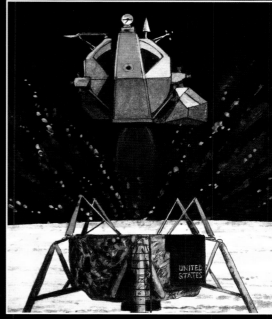

"THERE THEY GO, THE FIRST HUMANS IN HISTORY TO WALK ON THE MOON, STARTING A NEW EPOCH OF SPACE EXPLORATION!"

THREE HOURS, EIGHT MINUTES LATER...

EAGLE, I HAVE 0.7 MILES DISTANCE, APPROACHING AT 31 FEET PER SECOND.

APOLLO 13
DISASTER IN SPACE

13 APRIL 1970, 321,800 KILOMETRES FROM EARTH, 55 HOURS 46 MINUTES INTO THE MISSION...

...I'D LIKE TO END OUR BROADCAST BY SAYING THAT, FAR FROM BEING A SCARY PLACE, OUTER SPACE CAN ACTUALLY BE A LOT OF FUN!

COMMANDER JAMES LOVELL

THIS IS THE CREW OF APOLLO 13, WISHING EVERYBODY AT HOME A NICE EVENING...

WITHIN MINUTES...

OKAY, FUEL CELLS 1 AND 3 ARE SHOWING EMPTY AND YOUR OXYGEN LEVEL'S GOING DOWN TO ZERO. SO, WE ARE STARTING TO THINK ABOUT...

GLYNN LUNNEY IS THE FLIGHT DIRECTOR ON GOLD TEAM.

...THE LUNAR MODULE LIFEBOAT.

YES, WE'RE THINKING ABOUT THAT, TOO.

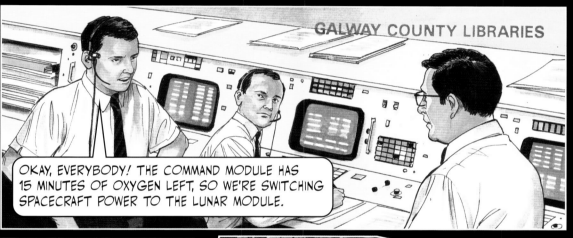

OKAY, EVERYBODY! THE COMMAND MODULE HAS 15 MINUTES OF OXYGEN LEFT, SO WE'RE SWITCHING SPACECRAFT POWER TO THE LUNAR MODULE.

BUT BEFORE ODYSSEY SHUTS DOWN, WE NEED TO PUT ITS GUIDANCE DATA INTO AQUARIUS OR...

...WE WON'T KNOW WHICH WAY WE'RE POINTING!

FRED, I'VE DONE THE MATHS. I'M COMING OVER!

GENE KRANZ IS FLIGHT DIRECTOR OF WHITE TEAM.

ON THIS SPACECRAFT, WHAT DO WE HAVE THAT'S STILL GOOD?

THEY HAVE ENOUGH OXYGEN, FOOD AND WATER TO LAST THE FOUR-DAY JOURNEY.

POWER IS GOING TO BE A PROBLEM.

THEY NEED TO MAKE SURE THERE'S ENOUGH CHARGE LEFT IN AQUARIUS'S BATTERIES* TO POWER ODYSSEY BACK UP WHEN THEY REACH EARTH, OR...

*UNLIKE ODYSSEY, AQUARIUS DIDN'T RUN OFF RENEWABLE FUEL CELLS.

...WE WON'T BE ABLE TO MAKE RE-ENTRY - UNDERSTOOD!

HOUSTON, I WAS THINKING, WOULD IT BE POSSIBLE TO BURN THE ENGINE AFTER WE ROUND THE MOON, TO ER, YOU KNOW, SPEED US UP A LITTLE?

GOOD IDEA, JACK, WE'LL MAKE THE CALCULATIONS.

35

14 APRIL, 16:21...

ZZZT...THIS IS HOUSTON. LOSS OF SIGNAL BEGINS IN FIVE SECONDS...FOUR...

BYE, BYE, EARTH. SEE YOU ON THE OTHER SIDE.

...THREE...TWO...ZZZZZZZZZ ...SHHHHHHHHHHHHHHHHHH...

MOON'S SO CLOSE, YOU CAN ALMOST TOUCH IT!

FEAST YOUR EYES FRED, NO ONE'S COMING BACK UP HERE FOR A LONG TIME*.

*ACTUALLY APOLLO 14 DID, NINE MONTHS LATER.

08:23...

HOUSTON, WE'RE READY TO BEGIN OUR TRANSEARTH INJECTION SEQUENCE*.

*FIRING OF THE ENGINE.

...OKAY, WE JUST NEED YOU TO CHECK GIMBAL SETTINGS AGAINST YOUR A.O.T.*

OKAY, TAKING A LOOK NOW...

*ALIGNMENT OPTICAL TELESCOPE – FOR SIGHTING STARS.

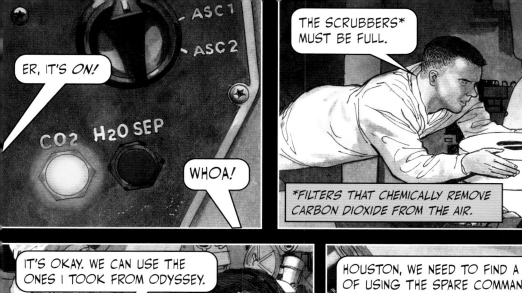

ER, IT'S *ON!*

WHOA!

THE SCRUBBERS* MUST BE FULL.

*FILTERS THAT CHEMICALLY REMOVE CARBON DIOXIDE FROM THE AIR.

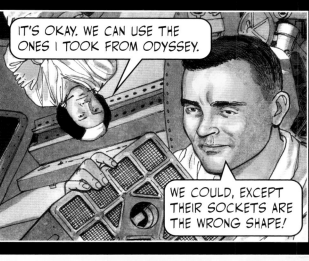

IT'S OKAY. WE CAN USE THE ONES I TOOK FROM ODYSSEY.

WE COULD, EXCEPT THEIR SOCKETS ARE THE WRONG SHAPE!

HOUSTON, WE NEED TO FIND A WAY OF USING THE SPARE COMMAND MODULE SCRUBBERS. ANY IDEAS?

WE'VE GOT SOMEONE WORKING ON IT. STAND BY.

WELL?

WE THINK IT'LL WORK...AS LONG AS THEY HAVE SOME DUCT TAPE ON BOARD.

17 APRIL, 10:10...

HOUSTON, ARE WE GOING TO HAVE ENOUGH AMPS FOR THE POWER-UP SEQUENCE? I MEAN, YOU *HAVE* TESTED IT, RIGHT?

THAT'S A NEGATIVE, 13. WE HAVEN'T HAD TIME FOR A HARDWARE TEST, BUT THE ENGINEERS ARE SURE IT WILL WORK.

IN THE CM...

*SHORT CIRCUIT.

PANEL'S SO DAMP, I'M MORE WORRIED ABOUT A SHORT*.

OKAY, 13. WE'RE READY TO GO.

GREAT, LET'S DO IT.

FOUR MINUTES LATER...

SERVICE MODULE JETTISONED!

LET'S TAKE A LOOK!

UNBELIEVABLE! THE WHOLE SIDE'S GONE.

FRANKLY, I'M AMAZED WE'RE ALIVE.

...BETTER GET SOME PICTURES.

SHUTTLES AND THE ISS

As the cost of the space programme increased, the USA looked for a cheaper alternative to getting people and satellites into space.

REUSABLE SPACECRAFT
A design for a spacecraft that could be reused was given the go-ahead in the 1970s. In 1981, the space shuttle *Columbia* flew into Earth orbit and returned safely. A new era in manned spaceflight had begun and a total of five space shuttles were built.

INTERNATIONAL SPACE STATION (ISS)
The Soviet Union collapsed in 1991 and the Cold War with it. A new spirit of cooperation in space meant that the USA, Russia and other countries around the world could now work together in building the ISS. The first part went into orbit in 1998 and it is due to be completed in 2010. Already, astronauts are spending six months at a time living and working in the ISS.

THE FUTURE IS ORION
After the loss of two shuttles and because of the programme's huge costs, the space shuttles will be taken out of service in 2010. A new spacecraft, called *Orion,* will replace them as part of Project Constellation, which will see us landing on the moon again.

The ISS (above) is still being assembled in Earth orbit. Replacement crews and supplies are ferried to the ISS by space shuttles (right) and by the Russian-built Soyuz TMA-7 *spacecraft (inset).*

44

Reusable shuttle

Reusable solid fuel rocket boosters

External fuel tank (not reusable)

Artist's impression of Orion and the lunar landing module.

GLOSSARY

abort To close down, or stop doing something, due to a problem.

airlock A small room with controllable air pressure and two entrances, which allows a person to pass between places with different air pressure, without air escaping.

altitude Height, usually above sea level.

amps Units of electrical current

CO_2 Carbon dioxide. A gas that we breathe out.

confirm To agree, or state that something is correct.

conquer To gain possession over someone or something by force.

cosmonaut A Russian astronaut.

crater A hole left in the ground where a meteorite has landed.

cryo tank Extremely cold tanks, containing liquid oxygen under pressure.

debris What remains when something is crushed or destroyed.

docking Joining with another, such as one spacecraft to another.

epoch A period of time.

fuel cell A device that produces an electric current from a chemical reaction, using oxygen and hydrogen.

gravity The force of attraction that exists between two bodies.

ignition Starting an engine by lighting it, usually with a spark.

jettison To throw cargo overboard in order to lighten a vehicle.

particle A tiny amount of matter, such as a molecule, atom or electron.

pressurised Compressed to a certain amount to maintain, in this case, an atmosphere that humans can survive in. When entering space from an airlock, the air has to be let out slowly. This is called depressurisation.

probe An unmanned spacecraft that records and sends to Earth information about the environment it is passing through.

quarantine A place where people are kept away from others, so that germs cannot be passed on.

renewable Something that can replenish or replace itself.

satellite Any object in orbit around a larger object - the Moon is a natural satellite of the Earth.

transposition When two things are switched around.

vacuum A space where there is no matter.

velocity Speed.

venting Discharging or blowing out something.

FOR MORE INFORMATION

ORGANISATIONS

National Space Centre
Exploration Drive
Leicester
LE4 5NS
0870 607 7223
E-mail: info@spacecentre.co.uk
Website: http://www.spacecentre.co.uk

Science Museum
Exhibition Road
South Kensington
London
SW7 2DD
0870 870 4868
E-mail: feedback@nmsi.ac.uk
Website: http://www.sciencemuseum.org.uk

FURTHER READING

Clarke, Penny. *The Story of the Exploration of Space*. Brighton: Book House, 2007.

Kerrod, Robin. *The Oxford Children's A-Z of Space 2004*. Oxford: Oxford University Press, 2004.

Malam, John. *First Man on the Moon: 21 July 1969* (Dates with History). London: Cherrytree Books, 2003.

Parker, Steve. *How it Works Space Exploration*. Great Bardfield: Miles Kelly Publishing Ltd, 2009.

Stott, Carole. *Space Exploration* (Eyewitness). London: Dorling Kindersley, 2002.

INDEX